Tom and Ricky

and the

Dancing Monkey

Bob Wright

High Noon Books
Novato

Cover Design: Nancy Peach
Interior Illustrations: Herb Heidinger

Glossary: basket, video, window, purse, banana

International Standard Book Number: 0-87879-360-7

9 8 7 6 5 4
5 4 3 2 1 0 9 8

You'll enjoy all the High Noon Books. Write for
a free full list of titles.

Contents

CHAPTER 1

His Name Is Peppy

Tom and Ricky were out riding their dirt bikes. Patches was with them. They were on Front Street when they saw Eddie.

"Look. There's Eddie," Ricky called out.

"Eddie! Eddie!" Tom yelled.

Eddie saw Tom and Ricky. He rode his dirt bike over to them.

"Are you going to the video store?" Tom asked. Tom and Ricky knew that Eddie liked to go there a lot.

"No. Not today," Eddie said.

"Want to ride around with us?" Ricky asked.

"No. I'm going over to Mr. King's store," Eddie answered.

"What for?" Tom asked.

"Mr. King has a man with a monkey," Eddie answered.

"A monkey? A big one?" Ricky asked.

"No. This is a little monkey. It does all kinds of tricks. Then people give it money for dancing. You should see it. It really is funny," Eddie said.

"No kidding," Tom said.

"That's right," Eddie said.

"Why did Mr. King get the monkey?" Tom asked.

"He said it's a good way to get people to come to his store," Eddie answered.

"Come to his store?" Ricky asked.

"Yes. You see, the monkey will be there for just three days. The monkey doesn't dance all day long. After the people watch the monkey, they go into the store. Then they buy things," Eddie said.

"That's a good idea," Ricky said.

"What's the monkey's name?" Tom asked.

"Peppy," Eddie answered.

"Peppy?" Tom said.

"Yes, Peppy," Eddie said.

"That's a funny name," Tom said.

"Wait until you see that little monkey jump all over the place. Then you'll see why he's called Peppy," Eddie said.

"Well, let's get going," Ricky said.

They all got on their dirt bikes. Then they started for Mr. King's store.

CHAPTER 2

Mr. King's Store

There were a lot of people at Mr. King's store. They were waiting for the monkey to come out.

"Look at all those people. They are waiting to see Peppy," Eddie said.

They all got off their bikes and locked them.

"Come on. Let's see if we can get close," Tom said.

Then they saw a little man come out in front of the store. The man had a little hat on his head.

"Look! There's Peppy," Eddie said.

Peppy was in a little basket. The man carried the basket with him.

Peppy sat up in the basket. He had a little hat on his head. The little monkey jumped out of the basket. Peppy had a long rope. This kept Peppy from going too far away from the man. The man started to play some music. Then Peppy started to dance. Everyone laughed.

"Look at Peppy. Look at the way he jumps around to the music," Ricky said.

All the people looked at Peppy. The man seemed happy.

"I'd sure like to take Peppy home with me," Tom said.

"Me, too," Eddie said.

The man stopped the music. Peppy stopped dancing. Then people gave Peppy money. He took it in his little hands.

Then Peppy started to dance.

"What will he do now?" Tom asked.

Peppy put the money in a little bag he carried.

"Will he do more tricks?" Tom asked.

"Yes. Wait," Eddie said.

Peppy's bag was full of money. Then he jumped into the basket. He dumped all of the money in the basket. Then he jumped down to get more money.

"The people sure like what he does," Tom said.

"They sure do," Eddie said.

Then the man started the music again. Peppy started to do more tricks. The people liked Peppy. They all laughed.

People gave Peppy more money. Each time he got money, he jumped in the basket to leave it there.

Mr. King was looking at all the people. Then he said, "Peppy must rest. He will dance again. The store is open now. Please come in."

Tom walked up to the man holding Peppy. "When will you be back with Peppy?"

"I must go now. Peppy must rest. You will see him again tomorrow," the man said.

Peppy sat down in the basket. The man put a coat over him. The man walked off with Peppy.

The boys started to leave, too. "We can come back later," Eddie said.

Then Tom turned around. "Did you see that?"

"See what?" Ricky asked.

"I thought I saw Peppy jump out of the basket," Tom said.

"Peppy is tired. Why would he jump out of the basket?" Ricky asked.

"The man is walking away. He wouldn't let the monkey run off like that. Anyway, Peppy has a rope around him. He couldn't go far," Eddie said.

"But I'm sure I saw Peppy jump out of the basket," Tom said.

"Come on. We'll be back tomorrow. You were just seeing things," Ricky said.

"OK. OK," Tom said.

"Where are you going now?" Ricky asked Eddie.

"I think I'll go to the video store," Eddie said.

"Want to go there?" Ricky asked Tom.

"I can't. I have some things to do at home," Tom answered.

"I'll see you tomorrow," Eddie called out. He rode off for the video store.

Then Tom and Ricky left to go home.

CHAPTER 3

Missing Money

The next day Tom and Ricky went back to see Peppy again. They wanted to see all the tricks the little monkey could do. Eddie got to Mr. King's store first.

"Look. There's Eddie," Ricky said.

"And look at all the people. Mr. King must be happy to have Peppy. A lot of people are here to see that little monkey," Tom said.

"They sure are. They're all over the place," Ricky said.

"Eddie!" Ricky called out.

Eddie didn't hear Ricky. He was looking into the store.

Ricky called out again, "Eddie! Eddie!"

This time Eddie could hear Ricky. He went over to him.

"I just saw Sergeant Collins. Did you hear about Mr. King's store?" Eddie asked.

"No. What do you mean?" Ricky asked.

"Do you see those police?" Eddie asked.

"We sure do," Tom said.

"Mr. King got here early. He opened his store. There was money missing from the store. They don't know who did it. All they found was a little hole in a window," Eddie said.

"You're kidding," Ricky said.

Just then Sergeant Collins walked over to the three boys.

"Was all the money gone?" Ricky asked.

"Yes, everything. Every night Mr. King puts all the money in a money box. Everything was missing from that box," the Sergeant said.

"Did many people know where Mr. King leaves the money each night?" Tom asked.

"No. Mr. King said that he puts the money box in a safe place," the Sergeant said.

"Eddie said there is a little hole in a window. What about that?" Ricky asked.

"That hole is very small. We don't know who made that hole," the Sergeant said.

"What does that hole have to do with all of this?" Ricky asked.

"We think it has something to do with the missing money," Sergeant Collins said.

"Look. Here comes the man with Peppy," Tom said.

Peppy sat up in the basket.

"That little monkey looks tired," Ricky said.

"He sure does," Eddie said.

There were a lot of people. They were waiting to see Peppy do his tricks. The man started to play the music. Peppy just sat.

"Get out! Dance!" the man yelled at Peppy. Peppy looked up at the man. Then he jumped out of the basket. He started to dance.

"He isn't dancing like he did yesterday," Eddie said.

The people liked Peppy. The music stopped. They gave him money. He took it with his little hands. He put it in his little bag. Then he jumped up into the basket and put all of it there.

The music started again. Peppy danced some more.

Now Peppy seemed to be having a good time. He jumped up on a woman. She didn't care. He opened her purse. He took out some money and gave it to the man. Everyone laughed.

"Peppy didn't put that money into the basket. He gave it right to the man," Ricky said.

"That was funny. Why did he do that?"

Eddie said.

The man said, "Bad Peppy."

He opened her purse. He took out some money.

Peppy took the money back to the woman. She wasn't mad. She thought it was funny.

Peppy started to go to another woman. The man pulled on the rope. Peppy fell over. "That is bad. Do not do that, Peppy," the man said.

Peppy looked hurt. Then he got up. The man started the music. Peppy started to dance again.

"That poor monkey. I hope he is all right," the woman said.

"He's OK," the man said.

People gave Peppy more money. Again, he got it, put it in his bag, and then took it to the basket.

"That is all for now," the man said.

Mr. King called out to everyone, "Come into the store. We are open. Peppy will be back again." Everyone started to go into the store.

Peppy sat in the basket. He saw the people going into the store.

All of a sudden, Peppy jumped out of the basket.

CHAPTER 4

A Big Mess

Peppy jumped out of the basket. The man didn't grab the rope. Peppy was free. He ran right into the store.

"What's going on?" Tom asked.

"Look at that! Peppy ran into the store," Ricky called out.

"Come here! Come here!" the man yelled.

Peppy didn't seem to hear the man. Everyone stopped and looked at him. Mr. King didn't know what to do.

Peppy jumped from one can to another. He ran all over the store. He didn't stop.

Cans were falling everywhere.

Cans were falling everywhere.

Peppy picked up apples. He slid all over. Everyone was laughing.

"Let's try to get him," Tom said.

"He's too fast and he's too small," Ricky said.

"That little monkey seems to know where everything is," Tom said.

The man outside started to play some music. He thought that Peppy would go back to him.

Then Peppy stopped. He ran over to the little hole in the window. He walked out. Then he jumped back into his basket.

"Bad Peppy," the man said. Then he hit Peppy.

Ricky ran outside. "Don't do that!" he said.

"Go away! I know what I am doing!" the man said. He looked mad at Peppy and Ricky.

Just then Sergeant Collins came to the store. "This place is a mess," he said.

"Peppy ran in the store. He was jumping all over," Tom said.

"The funny thing is that Peppy seemed to know where everything was," Ricky said.

"What do you mean?" Sergeant Collins asked.

"He was running all over the place. He didn't look mixed up," Ricky said.

"Who got him?" Sergeant Collins asked.

"No one. He ran out that little hole in the window," Ricky answered.

Just then Mr. King walked over to them. "I think I will have to close the store. I have to clean up this mess," he said.

"Will it take long to clean things up?" Ricky asked.

"Yes, it will. And Peppy will be back today to dance one more time," Mr. King said.

"We'll help you out," Ricky said.

Mr. King called out to everyone, "I must close the store. We will clean it up. Then we will open it up again." Everyone left the store.

A man stopped to talk to Mr. King. "Will Peppy be back today?" he asked.

"Yes, he will," Mr. King said as he looked around the store.

"Good. Then I will come back," the man said.

Tom, Ricky, and Eddie stayed with Mr. King in the store. They all picked up cans and put them back in place.

All of a sudden, Mr. King yelled, "More money is missing. Someone took more money!"

Tom and Ricky ran over to him.

"Look. I had more money in this money box. Now some of it is gone!" he yelled.

Sergeant Collins came over to Mr. King.

"All the people are out. But there were a lot of people in the store. Everyone was looking at Peppy. Someone took it at that time," the Sergeant said.

"This just can't be. I got Peppy to help out. Now more money is missing," Mr. King said.

"Everything is all cleaned up," Tom said.

"Look! Here comes the man with Peppy. They are ready to start again," Eddie said.

"Maybe Peppy should not do any more tricks today," Mr. King said.

"Here come three more police. We will see that everything goes OK," the Sergeant said.

"I will keep the store closed this time," Mr. King said. They all went outside.

"Is anyone in the store, Mr. King?" the Sergeant asked.

"No one. Everyone is out here. I have locked the store," Mr. King said.

"This time no money will be missing," Tom said.

"We'll see," Sergeant Collins said.

CHAPTER 5

Peppy Does It Again

Peppy sat up in his basket. Everyone was waiting to see what he would do. There were a lot of people waiting for Peppy to do his tricks.

"OK, Peppy. You can dance now," the man said.

The man started the music. Peppy jumped out of the basket. He started to do his tricks.

The people liked everything he did. Everyone laughed at his tricks. They wanted him to do more of them.

Then the music stopped. Peppy walked around. People gave him money. He put it in his little bag. Then he took it up to his basket.

Peppy jumped out of the basket. The man started the music. Peppy started to dance.

Then Peppy grabbed the rope. He pulled on it. The man stopped the music. Peppy pulled free. He ran up to the store.

"Oh, no. Not again," Eddie said.

"Come here! Come back here!" the man yelled.

"Don't worry. The store is locked. He can't get in," Mr. King called out.

Peppy ran over to the hole in the window.

"Look! He got into the store!" Ricky said.

Mr. King ran to the door. "Peppy isn't going to make another mess," he said.

All of a sudden Peppy came back out of the hole in the window.

But this time he had a lot of money in his little hands. Everyone looked at him. He ran up to the man with the music. He gave him all the money.

"No, Peppy. That is not our money. We must give that back," the man said.

Peppy just looked at the man.

"Here, Mr. King. Peppy is bad. This is your money. I don't know why he did that," the man said. The man looked mad at Peppy. He hit Peppy.

Mr. King took the money.

Peppy jumped up on Mr. King. He grabbed the money. He took it back to the man.

"What's going on?" Ricky said to Tom.

"I don't know," Tom said.

"Peppy is bad! That is not Peppy's money," the man said. He took the money from Peppy.

All of a sudden, Peppy opened the man's coat. He put his little hands inside. He started to pull out money, money, money.

The man grabbed Peppy. He pushed him down into the basket.

Everyone was looking at the man. No one was laughing.

"I think we will go now," the man said.

"Wait. Where did you get all that money?"

Sergeant Collins asked.

The man looked at Sergeant Collins.

He started to pull out money, money, money.

"I will go. I don't like people who say that Peppy takes money," the man said.

"I didn't say that. I just asked where you got all that money," Sergeant Collins said.

"I think we should have a little talk. Peppy has been bad," the man said.

"I think we all should go into the store. Mr. King, will you let us go in with you?" the Sergeant said.

Tom, Ricky, Eddie and Mr. King all went in with Sergeant Collins and the man and Peppy.

Mr. King looked at all the people. "Thank you for coming today to see Peppy. We will not open the store for the rest of the day," he said.

Everyone started to leave.

"You mean Peppy won't dance again today?" a woman asked.

"No. I'm sorry," Mr. King said.

They all went into the store.

Then Sergeant Collins said, "What's going on?"

The man looked at him. Peppy just sat in his basket. "What do you mean? Peppy has been bad. That's all there is to it," the man said.

"Let Peppy go. Let him out of the basket," the Sergeant said.

"Why do you want me to do that?" the man asked.

"I want to see where Peppy will go," Sergeant Collins said.

"But he will be bad again," the man said.

"Let him go," the Sergeant said.

The man took the rope off Peppy.

CHAPTER 6

The Surprise

Peppy jumped out of the basket. He looked all around. Then he started to run very fast.

Sergeant Collins looked at the boys. "See where he goes. We'll stay right here," he said.

Tom, Ricky, and Eddie walked in back of Peppy.

Peppy went right to where Mr. King put his money. He put his little hands in the money box. He grabbed some money. Then he ran back to the front of the store.

"Look at that! Peppy has more money," Mr. King said.

Peppy stopped. He looked at everyone. Then he went to the hole in the window.

"Don't let him out," Sergeant Collins called to Tom and Ricky.

Then Peppy went back to the man. He gave him all the money.

"What do you know? He gave me all the money," the man said. He looked surprised.

"Why are you surprised?" Sergeant Collins asked.

"What do you mean?" the man asked.

"Peppy danced for money. He gave all the money to you," Sergeant Collins said.

Ricky looked at Mr. King. "Was Peppy ever in the store?"

"Yes. He was. A week ago. That's when I asked this man to come back with Peppy," Mr. King answered.

"Did Peppy see where you put the money from the store?" Ricky asked.

"No. Wait! Yes, he did. But I didn't think anything about it," Mr. King answered.

"Now I see what this is all about," Sergeant Collins said.

"What do you mean?" the man asked.

"You left Peppy in the store last night. Then you made a little hole in the window. That's how he got out," Sergeant Collins said.

Then Tom said, "That's why Peppy looked so tired this morning!"

"That's right. He was in the store all night long," Sergeant Collins said.

"And he was all alone," Ricky said.

"You don't know what you're talking about," the man said.

"Then why did Peppy go back into the store and get more money today?" the Sergeant asked.

"And why did he go and get more money right now?" Ricky asked.

"This is all wrong. Peppy is bad sometimes. But he is not that bad," the man said.

"It isn't Peppy. It's you. You made him take the money," Sergeant Collins said.

"That's right. He was just doing what you wanted him to do," Ricky said.

"Peppy took money from your coat. You must have more in there," Sergeant Collins said.

"That's my money. You can't take it," the man said.

"I think you better come with me," Sergeant Collins said.

The man just looked as Sergeant Collins read him his rights.

"What about Peppy?" Tom asked.

"Peppy doesn't have to go. Can you boys keep him for a few days?" Sergeant Collins asked.

"Can we? Sure we can!" Tom said.

Sergeant Collins started to leave with the man. "You won't be hitting Peppy any more," the Sergeant said.

Mr. King called out, "I'll let you know how much money is missing."

"Good. We'll see how much he has on him," the Sergeant said.

Peppy sat in his basket. He looked at the man walking away.

"Can we give Peppy something to eat?" Ricky asked Mr. King.

"You sure can. I have a very nice banana I think he will like," Mr. King said.

Peppy took the banana and ate it very fast.

"I think he liked that banana," Tom said.

"He can have as many as he likes," Mr. King said.

He gave Peppy two more.

Peppy took the banana and ate it very fast.

"What will you do with Peppy?" Mr. King asked.

"We'd like to keep him. But I think Peppy would like to be with other monkeys," Eddie said.

"You know what? I think we all had better go home. I'm tired," Mr. King said.

"So are we," Ricky said.

"And so is Peppy. Look! He fell asleep on the bananas!" Tom said.